THRASS
TEACHING HANDWRITING READING AND SPELLING SKILLS

THRASS 500 WORKBOOK

Alan Davies

FOR READING, SPELLING, ANALYSING AND SYNTHESIZING
THE FIVE-HUNDRED BASEWORDS OF ENGLISH,
THROUGHOUT THE TEN STAGES OF TEACHING THRASS

a	⊖⊖⊖	a
about	⊖⊖⊖	a – b ou t
above	⊖⊖⊖	a – b o ve
across	⊖⊖⊖	a – c r o ss
after	⊖⊖⊖	a f – t er
again	⊖⊖⊖	a – g ai n
all	⊖⊖⊖	a ll
almost	⊖⊖⊖	a l – w ay s
along	⊖⊖⊖	a – l o ng
also	⊖⊖⊖	a l – s o
always	⊖⊖⊖	a l – w ay s
am	⊖⊖⊖	a m
an	⊖⊖⊖	a n
and	⊖⊖⊖	a n d
animals	⊖⊖⊖	a – n i – m a l s
another	⊖⊖⊖	a – n o – th er
ant	⊖⊖⊖	a n t
any	⊖⊖⊖	a – n y
April	⊖⊖⊖	A – p r i l
are	⊖⊖⊖	are

around	⊖⊖⊖	a – r ou n d
as	⊖⊖⊖	a s
asked	⊖⊖⊖	a s k ed
at	⊖⊖⊖	a t
August	⊖⊖⊖	Au – g u s t
away	⊖⊖⊖	a – w ay
baby	⊖⊖⊖	b a – b y
back	⊖⊖⊖	b a ck
ball	⊖⊖⊖	b a ll
balloon	⊖⊖⊖	b a – ll oo n
banana	⊖⊖⊖	b a – n a – n a
be	⊖⊖⊖	b e
beach	⊖⊖⊖	b ea ch
bear	⊖⊖⊖	b ear
because	⊖⊖⊖	b e – c au se
bed	⊖⊖⊖	b e d
bee	⊖⊖⊖	b ee
been	⊖⊖⊖	b ee n
before	⊖⊖⊖	b e – f ore
began	⊖⊖⊖	b e – g a n

being	⊖⊖⊖	b e – i ng
bell	⊖⊖⊖	b e ll
below	⊖⊖⊖	b e – l ow
better	⊖⊖⊖	b e – tt er
between	⊖⊖⊖	b e – t w ee n
big	⊖⊖⊖	b i g
bird	⊖⊖⊖	b ir d
birthday	⊖⊖⊖	b ir th – d ay
black	⊖⊖⊖	b l a ck
blue	⊖⊖⊖	b l ue
boat	⊖⊖⊖	b oa t
boil	⊖⊖⊖	b oi l
book	⊖⊖⊖	b oo k
both	⊖⊖⊖	b o th
box	⊖⊖⊖	b o <u>x</u>
boy	⊖⊖⊖	b oy
bread	⊖⊖⊖	b r ea d
break	⊖⊖⊖	b r ea k
bridge	⊖⊖⊖	b r i dge
brother	⊖⊖⊖	b r o – th er

brought	⊖⊖⊖	b r ough t
brown	⊖⊖⊖	b r ow n
bull	⊖⊖⊖	b u ll
buoy	⊖⊖⊖	b uoy
bus	⊖⊖⊖	b u s
but	⊖⊖⊖	b u t
buy	⊖⊖⊖	b uy
by	⊖⊖⊖	b y
cage	⊖⊖⊖	c a ge
called	⊖⊖⊖	c a ll ed
came	⊖⊖⊖	c a̲ m e̲
can	⊖⊖⊖	c a n
can't	⊖⊖⊖	c a n t
car	⊖⊖⊖	c ar
cat	⊖⊖⊖	c a t
chair	⊖⊖⊖	ch air
change	⊖⊖⊖	ch a n ge
cheese	⊖⊖⊖	ch ee se
chef	⊖⊖⊖	ch e f
cherry	⊖⊖⊖	ch e – rr y

children	⊖⊖⊖	ch i l – d r e n
circus	⊖⊖⊖	c ir – c u s
city	⊖⊖⊖	c i – t y
closed	⊖⊖⊖	c l o s ed
clothes	⊖⊖⊖	c l o th es
coffee	⊖⊖⊖	c o – ff ee
coin	⊖⊖⊖	c oi n
collar	⊖⊖⊖	c o – ll ar
come	⊖⊖⊖	c o me
coming	⊖⊖⊖	c o - m i ng
computer	⊖⊖⊖	c o m – p u – t er
cough	⊖⊖⊖	c ough
could	⊖⊖⊖	c oul d
cow	⊖⊖⊖	c ow
Dad	⊖⊖⊖	D a d
day	⊖⊖⊖	d ay
Dear	⊖⊖⊖	D ear
December	⊖⊖⊖	D e - c e m - b er
deer	⊖⊖⊖	d eer
did	⊖⊖⊖	d i d

didn't	⊖⊖⊖	d i d n t
different	⊖⊖⊖	d i ff – e – r e n t
dig	⊖⊖⊖	d i g
dinner	⊖⊖⊖	d i – nn er
dinosaur	⊖⊖⊖	d i – n o – s aur
do	⊖⊖⊖	d o
doctor	⊖⊖⊖	d o c – t or
does	⊖⊖⊖	d oe s
dog	⊖⊖⊖	d o g
dolphin	⊖⊖⊖	d o l – ph i n
don't	⊖⊖⊖	d o n' t
door	⊖⊖⊖	d oor
down	⊖⊖⊖	d ow n
Dr	⊖⊖⊖	<u>Dr</u>
dress	⊖⊖⊖	d r e ss
duck	⊖⊖⊖	d u ck
during	⊖⊖⊖	d <u>u</u> – r i ng
ear	⊖⊖⊖	ear
earth	⊖⊖⊖	ear th
eat	⊖⊖⊖	ea t

egg	⊖⊖⊖	e gg
eight	⊖⊖⊖	eigh t
eighteen	⊖⊖⊖	eigh – t ee n
eleven	⊖⊖⊖	e – l e – v e n
end	⊖⊖⊖	e n d
every	⊖⊖⊖	e – v e – r y
eyes	⊖⊖⊖	eye s
fair	⊖⊖⊖	f air
father	⊖⊖⊖	f a – th er
feather	⊖⊖⊖	f ea – th er
February	⊖⊖⊖	F e b - r u - a - ry
felt	⊖⊖⊖	f e l t
fern	⊖⊖⊖	f er n
field	⊖⊖⊖	f ie l d
fifteen	⊖⊖⊖	f i f – t ee n
finger	⊖⊖⊖	f i n – g er
fire	⊖⊖⊖	f ire
first	⊖⊖⊖	f ir s t
fish	⊖⊖⊖	f i sh
five	⊖⊖⊖	f i ve

fizz	⊖⊖⊖	f i zz
flu	⊖⊖⊖	f l u
fly	⊖⊖⊖	f l y
following	⊖⊖⊖	f o – ll o w – i ng
foot	⊖⊖⊖	f oo t
for	⊖⊖⊖	f or
forest	⊖⊖⊖	f o – r e s t
fork	⊖⊖⊖	f or k
fossil	⊖⊖⊖	f o – ss i l
found	⊖⊖⊖	f ou n d
four	⊖⊖⊖	f our
fourteen	⊖⊖⊖	f our – t ee n
free	⊖⊖⊖	f r ee
Friday	⊖⊖⊖	F r i – d ay
friends	⊖⊖⊖	f r ie n d s
frog	⊖⊖⊖	f r o g
from	⊖⊖⊖	f r o m
fruit	⊖⊖⊖	f r ui t
full	⊖⊖⊖	f u ll
fur	⊖⊖⊖	f ur

garden	⊖⊖⊖	g ar – d e n
gate	⊖⊖⊖	g <u>a</u> t <u>e</u>
get	⊖⊖⊖	g e t
giant	⊖⊖⊖	g i – a n t
girl	⊖⊖⊖	g ir l
give	⊖⊖⊖	g i ve
glove	⊖⊖⊖	g l o ve
glue	⊖⊖⊖	g l ue
go	⊖⊖⊖	g o
goes	⊖⊖⊖	g oe s
going	⊖⊖⊖	g o – i ng
gone	⊖⊖⊖	g o ne
good	⊖⊖⊖	g oo d
got	⊖⊖⊖	g ot
great	⊖⊖⊖	g r ea t
green	⊖⊖⊖	g r ee n
grey	⊖⊖⊖	g r ey
had	⊖⊖⊖	h a d
hair	⊖⊖⊖	h air
half	⊖⊖⊖	h a l f

hammer	⊖⊖⊖	h a – mm er
hand	⊖⊖⊖	h a n d
happy	⊖⊖⊖	h a – pp y
has	⊖⊖⊖	h a s
have	⊖⊖⊖	h a ve
he	⊖⊖⊖	h e
head	⊖⊖⊖	h ea d
hear	⊖⊖⊖	h ear
heard	⊖⊖⊖	h ear d
heart	⊖⊖⊖	h ear t
hedge	⊖⊖⊖	h e dge
Hello	⊖⊖⊖	H e – ll o
help	⊖⊖⊖	h e l p
her	⊖⊖⊖	h er
here	⊖⊖⊖	h ere
high	⊖⊖⊖	h igh
him	⊖⊖⊖	h i m
hippo	⊖⊖⊖	h i – pp o
his	⊖⊖⊖	h i s
home	⊖⊖⊖	h o me

horse	⊖⊖⊖	h or se
hour	⊖⊖⊖	<u>hour</u>
house	⊖⊖⊖	h ou se
how	⊖⊖⊖	h ow
I	⊖⊖⊖	I
I'll	⊖⊖⊖	I ll
I'm	⊖⊖⊖	I m
ice	⊖⊖⊖	i ce
if	⊖⊖⊖	i f
important	⊖⊖⊖	i m - p or - t a n t
in	⊖⊖⊖	i n
ink	⊖⊖⊖	i n k
inside	⊖⊖⊖	i n – s <u>i</u> d <u>e</u>
is	⊖⊖⊖	i s
it	⊖⊖⊖	i t
jam	⊖⊖⊖	j a m
January	⊖⊖⊖	J a n - <u>u</u> - a - r y
join	⊖⊖⊖	j oi n
July	⊖⊖⊖	J u – l y
jumped	⊖⊖⊖	j u m p ed

June	⊖⊖⊖	J u ne
just	⊖⊖⊖	j u s t
keep	⊖⊖⊖	k ee p
key	⊖⊖⊖	k ey
king	⊖⊖⊖	k i ng
kite	⊖⊖⊖	k i t e
kitten	⊖⊖⊖	k i – tt e n
knee	⊖⊖⊖	kn ee
knew	⊖⊖⊖	kn ew
know	⊖⊖⊖	kn ow
ladder	⊖⊖⊖	l a – dd er
lady	⊖⊖⊖	l a – d y
lamb	⊖⊖⊖	l a mb
laser	⊖⊖⊖	l a – s er
last	⊖⊖⊖	l a s t
laugh	⊖⊖⊖	l au gh
leave	⊖⊖⊖	l ea ve
left	⊖⊖⊖	l e f t
leg	⊖⊖⊖	l e g
letter	⊖⊖⊖	l e – tt er

light	⊖⊖⊖	l igh t
like	⊖⊖⊖	l i k e
lion	⊖⊖⊖	l i – o n
little	⊖⊖⊖	l i – tt l e
lived	⊖⊖⊖	l i v ed
long	⊖⊖⊖	l o ng
look	⊖⊖⊖	l oo k
lots	⊖⊖⊖	l o t s
love	⊖⊖⊖	l o ve
machine	⊖⊖⊖	m a – ch i ne
made	⊖⊖⊖	m a d e
make	⊖⊖⊖	m a k e
man	⊖⊖⊖	m a n
many	⊖⊖⊖	m a – n y
March	⊖⊖⊖	M ar ch
May	⊖⊖⊖	M ay
me	⊖⊖⊖	m e
measure	⊖⊖⊖	m ea – s ure
meet	⊖⊖⊖	m ee t
met	⊖⊖⊖	m e t

might	⊖⊖⊖	m igh t
Monday	⊖⊖⊖	M o n – d ay
money	⊖⊖⊖	m o – n ey
moon	⊖⊖⊖	m oo n
moor	⊖⊖⊖	m oor
more	⊖⊖⊖	m ore
morning	⊖⊖⊖	m or – n i ng
mother	⊖⊖⊖	m o – th er
motor	⊖⊖⊖	m o – t or
mouse	⊖⊖⊖	m ou se
Mr	⊖⊖⊖	<u>Mr</u>
Mrs	⊖⊖⊖	<u>Mrs</u>
Ms	⊖⊖⊖	<u>Ms</u>
much	⊖⊖⊖	m u ch
Mum	⊖⊖⊖	M u m
music	⊖⊖⊖	m <u>u</u> – s i c
must	⊖⊖⊖	m u s t
my	⊖⊖⊖	m y
name	⊖⊖⊖	n <u>a</u> m <u>e</u>
near	⊖⊖⊖	n ear

net	⊖⊖⊖	n e t
never	⊖⊖⊖	n e – v er
new	⊖⊖⊖	n <u>ew</u>
next	⊖⊖⊖	n e <u>x</u> t
night	⊖⊖⊖	n igh t
nine	⊖⊖⊖	n <u>i</u> n <u>e</u>
nineteen	⊖⊖⊖	n <u>i</u> n <u>e</u> – t ee n
no	⊖⊖⊖	n o
noise	⊖⊖⊖	n oi se
nose	⊖⊖⊖	n o se
not	⊖⊖⊖	n o t
note	⊖⊖⊖	n <u>o</u> t <u>e</u>
November	⊖⊖⊖	N o – v e m – b er
now	⊖⊖⊖	n ow
number	⊖⊖⊖	n u m – b er
o'clock	⊖⊖⊖	o – c l o ck
October	⊖⊖⊖	O c – t o – b er
of	⊖⊖⊖	o f
off	⊖⊖⊖	o ff
often	⊖⊖⊖	o f – t e n

old	⊖⊖⊖	o l d
on	⊖⊖⊖	o n
once	⊖⊖⊖	<u>o</u> n ce
one	⊖⊖⊖	<u>o</u> ne
only	⊖⊖⊖	o n – l y
opened	⊖⊖⊖	o – p e n ed
or	⊖⊖⊖	or
orange	⊖⊖⊖	o – r a n ge
other	⊖⊖⊖	o – th er
our	⊖⊖⊖	<u>our</u>
out	⊖⊖⊖	ou t
outside	⊖⊖⊖	ou t – s <u>i</u> d <u>e</u>
over	⊖⊖⊖	o – v er
owl	⊖⊖⊖	ow l
own	⊖⊖⊖	ow n
pair	⊖⊖⊖	p air
panda	⊖⊖⊖	p a n – d a
paper	⊖⊖⊖	p a – p er
park	⊖⊖⊖	p ar k
pear	⊖⊖⊖	p ear

people	⊖⊖⊖	p eo – p <u>l e</u>
piece	⊖⊖⊖	p ie ce
place	⊖⊖⊖	p l a ce
play	⊖⊖⊖	p l ay
please	⊖⊖⊖	p l ea se
plough	⊖⊖⊖	p l ough
point	⊖⊖⊖	p oi n t
police	⊖⊖⊖	p o – l i ce
pony	⊖⊖⊖	p o – n y
poor	⊖⊖⊖	p oor
pour	⊖⊖⊖	p our
pull	⊖⊖⊖	p u ll
purple	⊖⊖⊖	p ur – p <u>l e</u>
push	⊖⊖⊖	p u sh
put	⊖⊖⊖	p u t
queen	⊖⊖⊖	q u ee n
quick	⊖⊖⊖	q u i ck
quilt	⊖⊖⊖	q u i l t
rabbit	⊖⊖⊖	r a – bb i t
rain	⊖⊖⊖	r ai n

ran	⊖⊖⊖	r a n
read	⊖⊖⊖	r ea d
ready	⊖⊖⊖	r ea – d y
really	⊖⊖⊖	r e – a – ll y
red	⊖⊖⊖	r e d
right	⊖⊖⊖	r igh t
road	⊖⊖⊖	r oa d
rocket	⊖⊖⊖	r o – ck e t
round	⊖⊖⊖	r ou n d
said	⊖⊖⊖	s ai d
Saturday	⊖⊖⊖	S a – t ur – d ay
sauce	⊖⊖⊖	s au ce
saw	⊖⊖⊖	s aw
says	⊖⊖⊖	s ay s
school	⊖⊖⊖	s ch oo l
screw	⊖⊖⊖	s c r ew
sea	⊖⊖⊖	s ea
second	⊖⊖⊖	s e – c o n d
secret	⊖⊖⊖	s e – c r e t
see	⊖⊖⊖	s ee

seen	⊖⊖⊖	s ee n
September	⊖⊖⊖	S e p - t e m - b er
seven	⊖⊖⊖	s e − v e n
seventeen	⊖⊖⊖	s e − v e n - t ee n
shark	⊖⊖⊖	sh ar k
she	⊖⊖⊖	sh e
shirt	⊖⊖⊖	sh ir t
shop	⊖⊖⊖	sh o p
should	⊖⊖⊖	sh oul d
shout	⊖⊖⊖	sh ou t
show	⊖⊖⊖	sh ow
sister	⊖⊖⊖	s i s − t er
six	⊖⊖⊖	s i <u>x</u>
sixteen	⊖⊖⊖	s i <u>x</u> − t ee n
sleep	⊖⊖⊖	s l ee p
sleeve	⊖⊖⊖	s l ee ve
small	⊖⊖⊖	s m a ll
snail	⊖⊖⊖	s n ai l
sneeze	⊖⊖⊖	s n ee ze
snow	⊖⊖⊖	s n ow

so	⊖⊖⊖	s o
soap	⊖⊖⊖	s oa p
soil	⊖⊖⊖	s oi l
some	⊖⊖⊖	s o me
something	⊖⊖⊖	s o me – th i ng
sometimes	⊖⊖⊖	s o me – t i m e s
sound	⊖⊖⊖	s ou n d
square	⊖⊖⊖	s q u are
started	⊖⊖⊖	s t ar – t e d
station	⊖⊖⊖	s t a – ti o n
still	⊖⊖⊖	s t i ll
stopped	⊖⊖⊖	s t o pp ed
street	⊖⊖⊖	s t r ee t
such	⊖⊖⊖	s u ch
suddenly	⊖⊖⊖	s u – dd e n – l y
sun	⊖⊖⊖	s u n
Sunday	⊖⊖⊖	S u n – d ay
sure	⊖⊖⊖	s ure
swan	⊖⊖⊖	s w a n
swimming	⊖⊖⊖	s w i – mm i ng

table	⊖●⊖	t a – b l e
take	⊖⊖⊖	t a k e
tap	⊖⊖⊖	t a p
tape	⊖⊖⊖	t a p e
tea	⊖⊖⊖	t ea
teacher	⊖⊖⊖	t ea – ch er
teeth	⊖⊖⊖	t ee th
ten	⊖⊖⊖	t e n
than	⊖⊖⊖	th a n
that	⊖⊖⊖	th a t
the	⊖⊖⊖	th e
their	⊖⊖⊖	th eir
them	⊖⊖⊖	th e m
then	⊖⊖⊖	th e n
there	⊖⊖⊖	th ere
these	⊖⊖⊖	th e se
they	⊖⊖⊖	th ey
think	⊖⊖⊖	th i n k
thirteen	⊖⊖⊖	th ir – t ee n
this	⊖⊖⊖	th i s

those	⊖⊖⊖	th o se
thought	⊖⊖⊖	th ough t
three	⊖⊖⊖	th r ee
through	⊖⊖⊖	th r ough
thumb	⊖⊖⊖	th u mb
Thursday	⊖⊖⊖	Th ur s – d ay
tiger	⊖⊖⊖	t i – g er
time	⊖⊖⊖	t i m e
tin	⊖⊖⊖	t i n
to	⊖⊖⊖	t o
today	⊖⊖⊖	t o – d ay
together	⊖⊖⊖	t o – g e – th er
told	⊖⊖⊖	t o l d
too	⊖⊖⊖	t oo
took	⊖⊖⊖	t oo k
tour	⊖⊖⊖	t our
toy	⊖⊖⊖	t oy
tray	⊖⊖⊖	t r ay
treasure	⊖⊖⊖	t r ea – s ure
tree	⊖⊖⊖	t r ee

tries	⊖⊖⊖	t r ie s
Tuesday	⊖⊖⊖	T <u>ue</u> s – d ay
turned	⊖⊖⊖	t ur n ed
twelve	⊖⊖⊖	t w e l ve
twenty	⊖⊖⊖	t w e n – t y
two	⊖⊖⊖	tw o
under	⊖⊖⊖	u n – d er
until	⊖⊖⊖	u n – t i l
up	⊖⊖⊖	u p
upon	⊖⊖⊖	u – p o n
us	⊖⊖⊖	u s
used	⊖⊖⊖	<u>u</u> s ed
very	⊖⊖⊖	v e – r y
voice	⊖⊖⊖	v oi ce
walked	⊖⊖⊖	w al k ed
want	⊖⊖⊖	w a n t
was	⊖⊖⊖	w a s
wasp	⊖⊖⊖	w a s p
watch	⊖⊖⊖	w a tch
water	⊖⊖⊖	w a – t er

way	⊖⊖⊖	w ay
we	⊖⊖⊖	we
we're	⊖⊖⊖	w e're
Wednesday	⊖⊖⊖	W e <u>dnes</u> – d ay
went	⊖⊖⊖	w e n t
were	⊖⊖⊖	w ere
what	⊖⊖⊖	wh a t
wheel	⊖⊖⊖	wh ee l
when	⊖⊖⊖	wh e n
where	⊖⊖⊖	wh ere
while	⊖⊖⊖	wh <u>i</u> l <u>e</u>
white	⊖⊖⊖	wh <u>i</u> t <u>e</u>
who	⊖⊖⊖	wh o
whole	⊖⊖⊖	wh <u>o</u> l <u>e</u>
why	⊖⊖⊖	wh y
will	⊖⊖⊖	w i ll
window	⊖⊖⊖	w i n – d ow
with	⊖⊖⊖	w i th
without	⊖⊖⊖	w i th – ou t
woken	⊖⊖⊖	w o – k e n

woman	⊖⊖⊖	w o – m a n
won	⊖⊖⊖	w o n
wood	⊖⊖⊖	w oo d
word	⊖⊖⊖	w or d
work	⊖⊖⊖	w or k
world	⊖⊖⊖	w or l d
worm	⊖⊖⊖	w or m
would	⊖⊖⊖	w oul d
wrist	⊖⊖⊖	wr i s t
write	⊖⊖⊖	wr i t e
yawn	⊖⊖⊖	y aw n
year	⊖⊖⊖	y ear
yellow	⊖⊖⊖	y e – ll ow
yes	⊖⊖⊖	y e s
you	⊖⊖⊖	y ou
young	⊖⊖⊖	y ou ng
your	⊖⊖⊖	y our
zebra	⊖⊖⊖	z e – b r a
zero	⊖⊖⊖	z e – r o
zip	⊖⊖⊖	z i p

THRASS SPELLING PROCEDURE

The THRASS Spelling Procedure on pages 82 and 91 of TEACHING THRASS (T-50) is strongly recommended:

SAY: Say the word.
NAME: Name the letters.
COVER: Cover the word.
WRITE: Write the word.
CHECK: Check the letters.

Under the heading, FOCUS GRAPHEMES OR SEQUENCES, there is this advice on page 82:
"In the Name stage, it is not necessary to name all the letters if a learner is already able to visual some of them. Just name the letters that you need to concentrate on/visualise - this will be all the more memorable if you overwrite (trace over) the letter or letters in the word. Encourage groups or classes to discuss which graphemes, or sequences of letters, need to be visualised in the one-hundred-and-twenty-THRASSWORDS e.g. kitt-**e**-n, q-**u**-een, w-**a**-tch, treas-**ure** and some of the THRASS 500 basewords e.g. s-**ai**-d, **eigh**-t, th-**ere**, th-**eir**, bec-**au**-se and We-**dnes**-day...."

When it comes to using the THRASS SPELLING TILES (T-57), pick out and name the letter or letters that you need to concentrate on/visualise so that the letters become more memorable.

CORRECT SPELLING

a	ai	que	eigh	or	dnes
w<u>o</u>tch	s<u>e</u>d	mo<u>s</u>k	<u>ay</u>t	vect<u>er</u>	Wen<u>z</u>day

When correcting spelling, teachers are advised to underline the part of the word where there is a problem and to write the correct letter or sequence of letters above it. This indicates to the learner that the word should be entered into their Spelling Log (a plain or lined exercise book) and, when it comes to the NAME step of the THRASS Spelling Procedure, to overwrite (trace over) the focus letter or letters.

Ideally, if a letter is part of a digraph, trigraph or quad, it is best to write the complete grapheme rather than just an individual letter. For example, underlining the 'e' in vect<u>o</u>r only helps with the word vector but underlining the vowel digraph 'e' 'r' and writing 'o' 'r' helps with lots of other words in the same word family e.g. actor, tractor, doctor, sailor, councillor, donor, motor, squalor and so on. Similarly, overwriting the 'a' in watch helps with the spelling of was; overwriting the 'a' 'i' in said helps with the spelling of again; overwriting the 'q' 'u' 'e' helps with the spelling of plaque and overwriting the 'e' 'i' 'g' 'h' helps with the spelling of neigh. Rarely, the focus letter or letters may not be a grapheme. The 'u' in m<u>u</u>sic, the 'e' 'w' in n<u>ew</u> and the '<u>'</u>'n' 'e' 's' in We<u>dnes</u>day are NPS – "Not Playing Sensibly" (TEACHING THRASS, page 71).

Davies, A. & Ritchie, D. (2003) TEACHING THRASS. Publisher: THRASS UK, Chester, England. ISBN 1 904912 00 1. Copyright: Alan Davies. Code T-50